中华名胜导游系列画册

THE CLASSICAL GARDENS OF SUZHOU

苏州园林

蘇州園林

苏州市园林管理局
苏州市旅游管理局 合编
中国旅游出版社

中国旅游出版社

京新登字 031 号

〈苏州园林〉

主　　编:徐文涛

副 主 编:韩先云　黄敬如

摄　　影:郑可俊　陈健行　周仁德　谢新发　郑　翔

　　　　谷维恒　刘大健　牛嵩林　张克庆　刘英杰

　　　　周春燕　贾静安　周　全　白　亮

撰　　文:周　峥

特约编辑:周　峥

责任编辑:谷维恒　许　华

图片编辑:周仁德　许　华

图片提供:中国旅游出版社图片中心

〈中华名胜导游系列画册〉主编:谷维恒

英文翻译:董晓明

日文翻译:孙来庆

绘图:傅马力

图书在版编目(CIP)数据

苏州园林/徐文涛主编.－北京:中国旅游出版社,19·

96.8

(中华名胜导游系列画册/谷维恒主编)

ISBN 7－5032－1312－4

Ⅰ.苏…　Ⅱ.徐…　Ⅲ.古典园林－中国－苏州－画册Ⅳ.

K928.73－64

中国版本图书馆 CIP 数据核字(96)第 14765

目录

Contents

3

前言

上有天堂，下有苏杭。

苏州，中国著名的历史文化名城，素以众多精雅的园林名闻天下。苏州地处长江三角洲，地理位置优越，气候湿润，交通便利，旧时官宦名绅退休后多到苏州择地造园、颐养天年。

明清时期，苏州封建经济文化发展达到鼎盛阶段，造园艺术也趋于成熟，出现了一批园林艺术家，使造园活动达到高潮。最盛时苏州的私家园林和庭院达280余处，至今保存完好并开放的有，始建于宋代的沧浪亭、网师园，元代的狮子林，明代的拙政园、艺圃，清代的留园、耦园、怡园、曲园、听枫园等。其中，拙政园、留园因其精美卓绝的造园艺术和个性鲜明的艺术特点，与北京颐和园、承德避暑山庄被公誉为中国四大名园。

苏州园林是城市中充满自然意趣的"城市山林"，身居闹市的人们一进入园林，便可享受到大自然的"山水林泉之乐"。在这个浓缩的"自然界"，"一勺代水，一拳代山"，园内的四季晨昏变化和春秋草木枯荣以及山水花木的季相变化，使人们可以"不出城郭而获山林之怡，身居闹市而有林泉之乐"。

苏州园林是文化意蕴深厚的"文人写意山水园"。古代的造园者都有很高的文化修养，能诗善画，造园时多以画为本，以诗为题，通过凿池堆山、栽花种树，创造出具有诗情画意的景观，被称作是"无声的诗，立体的画"。在园林中游赏，犹如在品诗，又如在赏画。为了表达园主的情趣、理想、追求，园林建筑与景观又有匾额、楹联之类的诗文题刻，有以清幽的荷香自喻人品（拙政园"远香堂"），有以清雅的香草自喻性情高洁（拙政园"香洲"），有追慕古人似小船自由漂荡怡然自得的（怡园"画舫斋"），还有表现园主企慕恬淡的

4

田园生活的(网师园"真意"、留园"小桃源")等等,不一而足。这些充满着书卷气的诗文题刻与园内的建筑、山水、花木自然和谐地揉和在一起,使园林的一山一水、一草一木均产生出深远的意境,倘佯其中,可得到心灵的陶冶和美的享受。

苏州园林虽小,但古代造园家通过各种艺术手法,独具匠心地创造出丰富多样的景致,在园中行游,或见"庭院深深深几许",或见"柳暗花明又一村",或见小桥流水、粉墙黛瓦,或见曲径通幽、峰回路转,或是步移景易、变幻无穷。至于那些形式各异、图案精致的花窗,那些如锦缎般的在脚下延伸不尽的铺路,那些似不经意散落在各个墙角的小品……更使人观之不尽,回味无穷。

FOREWORD

Up in heaven there's a paradise; down on earth there're Suzhou and Hangzhou.

Situated in the Lower Yangtze Delta, Suzhou boasts favorable location, mild climate, convenient traffic, and a large number of classical gardens. It has been a famous historical and cultural city in China, an ideal place where many officials and scholars in times past purchased and planned their garden-residences as retreats for their retirement years. During the Ming and Qing Dynasties, Suzhou saw a perod of feudal economic prosperity and cultural flowering. Consequently, the number of privately-owned gardens in the city of Suzhou and its environs increased a great deal, mounting to 280 odd. A galaxy of great masters emerged and the art of landscape gardening reached its apogee. Many have survived to the present day and are open to the public such as the Canglang Pavilion and the Master-of-Nets Garden first built under the Song, the

Lion Forest Garden under the Yuan, the Humble Administrator's Garden and the Garden of Cultivation under the Ming, the Lingering Garden, the Couple's Garden Retreat, the Garden of Pleasance, the Zigzag Garden and the Listening to Maple Garden under the Qing. The Humble Administrator's Garden and the Lingering Garden, noted for their artistic perfection and individual characteristics, are known as China's four most famous gardens along with the Summer Palace in Beijing and the Imperial Mountain Resort in Chengde. A Suzhou garden is the origination of "urban scenery", a microcosm of the world made of the basic elements of water, rocks, plants and buildings, which are arranged in such a way that they reflect the sequential beauty in the garden—the passage of time, the dissimilarity between mornings and evenings, and the succession of the seasons within the boundary of the wall and lead a sequestered life amongst the bustling city.

Ancient Chinese garden builders were all highly educated, and good at verse and painting. Rich in literary allusions and analogous with the freehand brushwork in traditional Chinese painting, the classical gardens of Suzhou are the re-creation of nature through the processes of the decoration of land by planting trees, shrubs and flowers, and designing and materializing mountains and watercourses. Sometimes they are called "a silent poem and three-dimensional painting". Strolling through a garden is like appreciating the poetic works of a great master or unrolling a long scroll of Chinese landscape painting. Distinctively, garden buildings and beauty-spots have plateaux, inscribed stelae of great antiquity and parallel couplets in excellent calligraphy and tonal arrangement with the purpose of expressing owner's temperament, moral worth, deep feeling or noble thought. There are many instances in illustration of Chinese ethical, ideological and intellectual pursuits. The Hall of Drifting Fragrance in the Humble Administrator's Garden indicates that the owner wants to be as pure and clean as lotus blooms, and the Fragrant Isle, named after fragrant herbs, is emblematic of noble sentiments. Like an ancient hermit boat sailing about freely and happily, the Fancy Boat Study in the Garden of Pleasance is symbolic of the freedom of the will. The True Meaning in the Master-of-Nets Garden and the Small Utopia in the Lingering Garden are suggestive of the rustic simplicity of country life. Interwoven with these ideas, every rock, every waterway, every plant, and every part of the garden affords much food for thought. Indeed, the classical gardens of Suzhou are the places where people can cultivate their minds and take great pleasure in studying Chinese aesthetics. Employing extraordinary methods and techniques in olden days, the garden builder successfully created within limits endless varieties of perspectives, dazzling the eye as well as the mind. The garden is full of surprises. The view is changing at every step. On a garden walk, there are countless different incidents—garden courts in succession, small bridges, murmuring brooks, whitewashed walls, grey roof-tiles, numerous latticed windows with intricate patterns, pathways winding up and down hills, and leading to places of quietude, mosaics and pavements with all kinds of delicate geometrics or representations of brocade, mini-gardens in out-of-the-way places, etc. It is impossible to explore and learn about them all. "With mountain chains and rivers ahead, you might think that there's no way through. Why, shady willows and brilliant flowers keep one more village out of sight. "In a word, there's an enchanting impression of infinitude.

前書き

　上に極楽あれば下に蘇州と杭州あり。

　蘇州は中国の著名な歴史文化の古都で、昔から数え切れないほどの精緻で優雅な園林でその名を天下に轟かせて来た。長江デルタ地帯の優越な地理位置に恵まれた蘇州は、気候が湿潤で交通が便利なので、旧時の高官や紳士たちは老後生活を楽しくするため、停年後、続々と蘇州に来て場所を選んで造園してきたのである。

　明代と清代の時、蘇州の封建経済文化の発展はその極まりに達し、造園芸術も次第に成熟し、多くの園林芸術家も現れて、造園活動が盛んになった。最盛期に蘇州には280ヵ所余りの私家園林や庭があった。今日まで完璧に保存され開放されているものには宋代の滄浪亭と網師園、元代の獅子林、明代の拙政園と芸圃、浦代の留園、耦園、怡園、曲園や聴楓園等がある。その内の拙政園と留園は精美卓越した造園芸術と個性鮮明な芸術特色によって、北京の頤和園と承徳の避暑山荘と共に中国の四大名園と誉められている。

　蘇州園林は都市の中での自然の趣に満ちた"都市山林"であり、賑やかな都市生活に居慣れた人々は園林に入ると、大自然の"山水林泉の楽しみ"を享楽することができる。この濃縮した山水の"自然界"では、四季の朝晩の変化と春秋草木の栄枯および山水花卉の異なるシーズンの変化よって、人々は"城郭を出なくても山林の趣が得られ、賑やかな市に居ながらも林泉の楽しみが味わえる"。

　蘇州園林は濃厚な文化息吹きに包まれる"文人墨客の写意山水園"である。古代の造園者は皆高い文化修養の持ち主で、作詩もでき絵画にも長ける者であった。園林を造営するに当たっ

て、それぞれ絵を元にし詩を題にするほか、池を掘ったり、築山を積み重ねたり、花を栽培したり、木を植えたりすることによって作り出した詩情画意に満ちた景観は“無声の詩と立体的な絵”と誉められている。このような庭園を遊べば丸で詩を吟味したりし、絵を鑑賞したりしているようである。庭園の持ち主が自分の趣や理想や追求などを表すため、園林建築と景観には詩文や題名を彫刻した額や対句などがある。例えば自らの人柄を清らかで奥床しく芳しい香りを放つ蓮に例える（拙政園の）“遠香堂”もあれば、自分の高潔な品性を香る草に例える（拙政園の）“香洲”もあり、川を自由自在に漂う小舟のような何も束縛もない古人を羨ましい（怡園の）“画舫斎”もあれば、庭園の持ち主が軽やかな田園生活を待ち望む（網師園の）“真意”と（留園の）“小桃源”などが――と例え切れないほどたくさんある。これらの学者気分に満ちた詩文や題名彫刻は園内の建築、山水、花木と何も作り気もなく調和よく一つに溶け合って、庭の一山一水、一木一草に深い意匠を生み出させたため、このような庭をゆっくりと観光すれば、心霊も陶冶され、美的享楽が得られる。

　蘇州の園林は敷地が狭いとは言え、古代の造園家たちは諸々の芸術手法を用い、創意工夫を凝らして、豊富多彩な景観を作り出した。庭を巡り歩けば、或いは“奥深さがどこまで続くのか”、或いは“柳暗くて花明らかに又一村”の景観。さもなれば小さい橋流れる水と白壁に黒瓦、曲がりくねった小道、一歩を歩くごとに景色が変わるという千変万化の景観が見える。形がそれぞれ違い精緻を極めたデザインの花窓や延々と続く錦のような美しい舗地やわざわざ作ったものでもないように見える隅々に散在する小品などは、どれもこれも人々にいつ、どこまで観賞しても切りがなく、長く味わわせる。

The Humble Administrator's Garden

1. The main gate

2. The Cymbidium Virens Hall

3. The Cloud Adornment Peak

4. The Lotus Pavilion

5. The Celestial Spring Pavilion

6. The Nice Smell of Rice House

7. The Far Away Looking Pavilion

8. The Leaning on Rainbow Pavilion

9. The Hall of Drifting Fragrance

10. The South Pavilion

11. The Orange Pavilion

12. The Prunus Mume Pavilion

13. The Pavilion in the Lotus Breezes

14. The Pine Wind Pavilion

15. The Small Canglang

16. "A Pure Mind Thinks Deep."

17. The True Nature Pavilion

18. Fragrant Isle

19. The Meditation Tower

20. The Magnolia Hall

21. The Moon Gate

22. The Good for Both Families Pavilion

23. The Hall of 36 Pairs of Mandarin Ducks

24. The Hall of 18 Camellias

25. The Pagoda Reflection Pavilion

26. The Stay and Listen Pavilion

27. The "With Whom Shall I Sit?" Pavilion

28. The Indocalamus Hat Pavilion

29. The Floating Green Pavilion

30. The Reflection Tower

31. The Mountain in View Tower

32. The Green Ripple Pavilion

33. The Secluded Pavilion of Firmiana Simp

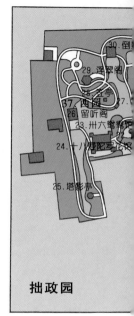

拙政园

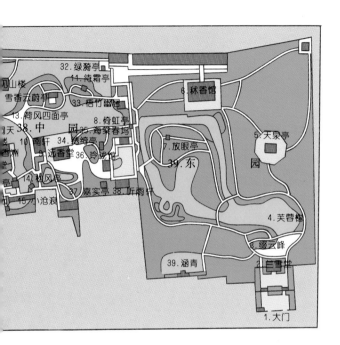

32.绿漪亭
11.待霜亭
6.秋香馆
观山楼
雪香云蔚亭
33.梧竹幽居
13.荷风四面亭
8.倚虹亭
38.中　　园 35.海棠春坞
5.天泉亭
天
10.南轩 34.资绮亭
7.放眼亭
园
香洲 远香堂 36.玲珑馆
39.东
14.松风亭
37.嘉实亭 38.听雨轩
4.芙蓉榭
45.小沧浪
3.缀云峰
39.涵青
2.兰雪堂
1.大门

一、拙政园

拙政园,位于苏州城东北部,占地面积约 78 亩,为苏州古典园林的代表作品,也是我国四大名园之一。1961 年被列为全国重点文物保护单位。拙政园始建于明朝正德四年(1509 年),御使王献臣被贬官后还乡建造,取晋代潘岳《闲居赋》"灌园鬻蔬,以供朝夕之膳,……是亦拙者之为政也"语意命名。嘉靖十二年(1533 年),著名画家文徵明曾依园景绘图卅一幅。现园分东、中、西三部分和部分住宅,布局因地制宜,以水池为中心,在清澄萦洄的水池和重嶂叠翠的林中,各式建筑临水而筑,格调古朴自然,呈现出池广树茂、旷远明瑟的明代江南园林特色。园西部为盆景园,陈列苏派盆景 700 余盆。住宅部分现为园林博物馆。

Ⅰ. The Humble Administrator's garden

Located in the northeastern part of the city of Suzhou, the Humble Administrator's Garden covers 51, 950 sq. m. , being a fine example of the classical gardens of Suzhou, and one of the four most famous gardens in China. It was listed as cultural relics of national importance in 1961. During the 4th year of the reign of Zhengde of the Ming Dynasty(1509 A. D.), the imperial inspector Wang Xianchen returned to Suzhou after retiring from public life and built his garden. He borrowed the idea from the essay by the Jin writer Pan Yue, saying, "To cultivate my garden and sell my vegetable crop… is the policy of humble man. "Hence the name. In the 12th year of the reign of Jiajing(1533 A. D.), the distinguished artist Wen Zhengming parnted 31 scrolls of paintings relevant to the garden. The Humble Administrator's Garden is divided into three parts: the eastern, middle and western parts. The house lies to the south of the garden. Making good use of the terrestrial contours of the site, the Humble Administrator's Garden is simple, extensive and natural with various kinds of buildings being centered upon the broad expanse of a crystalline lake and verdant hills reminiscent of the scenery in the south of the Lower Yangtze. Over 700 bonsai(potted landscape) are put on display in the Bonsai Garden in the western part of the garden, representing the Suzhou style bonsai. Part of the housing complex is now used as the Garden Museum.

一、拙政園

　蘇州の東北側に位置する拙政園は15600 坪の敷地面積をもち、蘇州の古典園林の代表作で、1961 年に全国重要文化財に指定され、中国四大名園の一つになっている。拙政園は明代の正徳四年(1509 年)、御史(主に官吏の弾劾を司る官職)王献臣が官職を落とされ故郷の蘇州に戻ってから営造されたものである。「拙政」という園名は、晋の時代の潘岳の《閑居賦》の中の「拙者之為政(愚劣な者が政を司ること)」から来たものである。嘉靖十二年(1533 年)、著名な画家文徴明が園景を31 枚の絵に描いた。拙政園は東部、中部、西部及び住宅部分からなっている。配置は地勢によって塩梅し、池を中心にしている。自然で古めかしい各種類の建築物は、澄み切っている池水に臨んで建てられたり、重なっている築山や生い茂っている林の間に築かれたりしていて、明代の江南園林の特色と雰囲気を醸し出している。拙政園の西部は今盆栽館になって、700 余りの蘇州式の盆栽が展示されている。その住宅部分は園林博物館になっている。

△ 兰雪堂内的漆画

The Lacquer Carving in the Cymbidium Virens Hall.

蘭雪堂内の漆絵

▽ 拙政园腰门

The side entrance to the Humble Administrator's Garden.

拙政園の二番目の入口

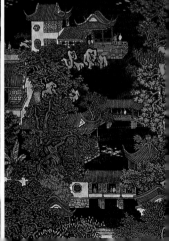

△ 芙蓉榭
The Lotus Pavilion.

芙蓉榭

◁ 远香堂，为中园主体建筑，系明代结构。

The Hall of Drifting Fragrance, the chief structure in the middle part of the garden, dating back to the Ming Dynasty.

遠香堂は中部の主建築で、明代の構築

◁ 远香堂的内部陈设

Furnishings of the Hall of Drifting Fragrance.

遠香堂内部の調度類

△ 临水而建的南轩

The South Pavilion built over the water.

水に臨んで建てられた南軒

▽ 荷风四面亭之晨

The Pavilion in Lotus Breezes in the morning.

荷風四面亭の朝

◁ 小飞虹，为苏州园林唯一的廊桥

The Small Flying Rainbow, a unique roofed bridge in the classical gardens of Suzhou.

小飛虹——蘇州園林にある唯一の廊橋

△ 五月的中园景色

The scene of the middle part of the garden in May.

五月の中部の景色

△ 这是一座旱船,下部名为香洲,上部称为澂观楼。

The two-storeyed boat-like structure, the first floor is called "the Fragrant Isle" and the second floor "the Meditation Tower".

一階は"香洲"で、

二階は"澂観楼"の不繋舟

△ 香洲夜色

The Fragrant Isle at night.

香洲の夜景

△ 春天的香洲
The Fragrant Isle in spring.
春の香洲

▷ 极为典雅的玉兰堂侧门
The side entrance to the elegant
Magnolia Hall.
頗る典雅な玉蘭堂の横門

◁ 别有洞天

A moon gate.

别有洞天

▽ 夏日的宜两亭

The Good-for-Both-Families Pavilion in summer.

夏の宜两亭

▷ 从西园看中园的雪景

A snowy view of the middle part of the garden from the western part of the garden.

西部から中部の雪景色を望む

▽ 环池修建的波形长廊极有特色

A long, wavy verandah built by the pool.

池に沿って築かれた特色ある波状の長い廊下

◁ 卅六鸳鸯馆内部陈设
Furnishings of the 36 Pairs of Mandarin Ducks' Hall.
卅六鴛鴦館内部の調度類

◁ 荷塘夏日
The lotus pool in summer.
夏の蓮池

△ 雪后见山楼
A snowy scene of the Mountain-in-View Tower.
見山楼の雪景色

△ 位于中园北部,临水而建的见山楼

The Mountain-in-View Tower built over the water in the north of the middle part of the garden.

水に臨んで建てられた見山楼

◁ 小山上待霜亭

The Orange Pavilion atop of the small H

待霜亭

△ 园中夜色

The Humble Administrator's Garden in the evening.

庭園の夜景

△ 梧竹幽居，四面设有园洞门。
The Secluded Pavilion of Firmiana
Simplex and Bamboo with moon
gates on four sides.
四面に円洞門のある梧竹幽居

▽ 四月，园中的牡丹花盛开
In April the peonies are open in the
Humble Administrator's Garden.
四月に満開する牡丹の花

▷ 海棠春坞内的铺地
The pavement of the Malus
Micromalus Makina Court.

海棠春坞の舗地

▽ 枇杷园,因院中种有枇杷
而得名。
The Loquat Garden named after
loquat trees growing in the
garden.

枇杷園

二、留园

留园,在苏州阊门外,面积约 30 亩,是我国四大名园之一,也是"吴中名园之冠"。1961 年被列为全国重点文物保护单位。明嘉靖年间太仆徐泰时置东、西二园(后西园改为寺院),于东园内广搜奇石,又请名师堆叠假山。清嘉庆时改名寒碧庄,并集太湖石十二峰于园内。光绪初重修,改名留园。现园分东、中、西、北四部分,东部以庭院、建筑取胜,中部是山水写意园,西部林木幽深、有山林野趣,北部竹篱小屋、呈田园风貌。留园以建筑空间艺术处理精湛著称,园以厅堂、走廊、粉墙、洞门等划分空间,通过与山水花木组合成一个个错落相联、层次丰富的庭院,体现了江南园林建筑的艺术特点。

Ⅱ. The Lingering Garden

With an area of 23,310 sq. m. , the Lingering Garden, one of the four most famous gardens in China and the best garden in Suzhou, is situated outside the Cang Gate of the city of Suzhou. In 1961 it was listed as cultural relics of national importance. During the 21st year of the reign of Wanli(1593 A. D.), Xu Taishi, carrying the ministerial title of Tai Pu Si Shao Qing, built his garden-residence called "the East Garden and the West Garden(it was later converted into a temple)". The well-known master Zhou Bingzhong was requested to build a range of awe-inspiring stone mountains in the East Garden. In the reign of Jiaqing, it, renamed "the Hanbi Villa", was celebrated for 12 limestone peaks hauled from Lake Tai. In the early years of the reign of Guang Xu, it was given a new name "the Lingering Garden" after repair. Today the garden is separated into the eastern, middle, northern and western parts. The middle part features man-made mountain and lake scenery , resembling a long scroll of traditional Chinese painting. The eastern part is noted for its happy groupings of garden courts and elegant buildings, the western part the enchantment of woody hills, and the northern part cottages with bamboo fences and idyllic scenes. The Lingering Garden sets excellent examples of how garden spaces are ingeniously handled. The garden is divided and subdivided by various kinds of buildings such as halls, rooms, roofed walkways and walls with moon gates into numerous garden courts, evoking countless perspectives through the decorative and functional alteration, and the landscaping of grounds by employing rocks, water, flowers and trees. It is characteristic of the classical gardens in the south of the Lower Yangtze.

二、留園

　　留園は蘇州の閶門外に位置し、6000 坪の敷地面積をもっている。留園は"呉中一の名園"で、1961 年に全国重要文化財に指定され、中国四大名園の一つになっている。明代の嘉靖年間、太僕(官職)徐泰時は東園と西園を営造した(西園は今お寺になっている)。彼は多くの奇岩怪石を集め、それを名匠に築山に積み重ねて貰った。清代の嘉慶年間に寒碧山荘に改名された時、12 枚の太湖石の怪石を園内に収めた。光緒年間の初期重修された時、今の留園に改名されたのである。庭園は東部、中部、西部と北部の四つの部分からなっている。東部は主に庭と建築物で、中部は山水の写意園で、西部は樹木の生い茂る岡があって山林野趣に富み、北部は竹の矢来と小さい家屋があり、田園風景を呈している。留園は建築スペースの傑出した芸術処理によって知られている。庭は庁、堂、廊下、白壁や洞門などによってスペースを分け、又山水花木との組合で一つ又一つの重なりあって、立体感に富む庭を作り出していることによって江南園林芸術の特徴を表している。

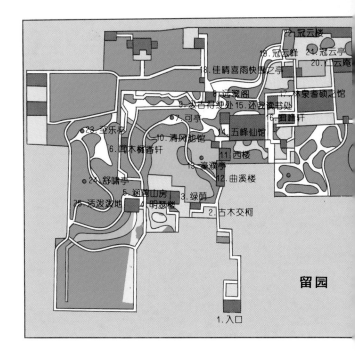

留园

1. 入口

The Lingering Garden

1. Entrance

2. Verdurous old trees

3. The Green Shade Pavilion

4. The Pellucid Tower

5. The Hanbi Mountain Villa

6. The Osmanthus Fragrans Pavilion

7. The Passable Pavilion

8. The Distant Green Pavilion

9. The Study of Enlightenment

10. The Refreshing Breeze Pavilion by the lake

11. The West Tower
12. The Zigzag Stream Tower
13. The Hao Pu Pavilion
14. The Celestial Hall of Five Peaks
15. The Return to Read Study
16. The Worshipping Stone Pavilion
17. The Old Hermit Scholars' House
18. The Good for Farming Pavilion

19. The Cloud Capped Peak
20. The Awaiting Cloud Temple
21. The Cloud Capped Pavilion
22. The Cloud Capped Tower
23. The Delightful Pavilion
24. The Free Roaring Pavilion
25. The Place of Liveliness

四、留園

1、入口
2、古木交柯
3、緑蔭
4、明瑟楼
5、涵碧山房
6、聞木樨香軒
7、可亭
8、遠翠閣
9、汲古得綆処
10、清風池館
11、西楼
12、曲渓楼
13、濠濮亭
14、五峰仙館
15、還我読書処
16、揖峰軒

17、林泉耆碩之館
18、佳晴喜雨快雪之亭
19、冠雲峰
20、仁雲庵
21、冠雲亭
22、冠雲楼
23、至楽亭
24、舒嘯亭
25、活溌溌地

▽ 明瑟楼窗景

Window pictures of the pellucid Tower.

明瑟楼の窓景色

◁ 春天的明瑟楼、曲溪楼与小蓬莱。
The Pellucid Tower, the Winding Stream Tower
and the Small Fairy Isle in spring.

春の明瑟楼、曲溪楼と小蓬莱

▽ 从绿荫轩望园中景色
A view of the middle part of the garden from
the Green Shade Pavilion.

緑蔭軒から望んだ園中の景色

◁ 明瑟楼

The Pellucid Tower.

明瑟楼

◁ 明瑟楼雪后

A snowy scene of the Pellucid Tower.

明瑟楼の雪景色

△ 小蓬莱与濠濮亭,为建在水面上的廊和亭

The Small Fairy Isle of the lake and the Hao Pu Pavilion built over the water.

小蓬莱と濠濮亭は水面上に建てられた廊と亭

△ 园内西部的景色　西部の景色
The scene of the western part of the
Lingering Garden.

▽ 临池而建的清风池馆和濠濮亭。
The Refreshing Breeze Pavilion and the Hao
Pu Pavilion built over the water.

に臨んで建てられた清風池館と

僕亭

△ 又一村,现为盆景园。

Another Village（the Bonsai Garden now）

又一村にある盆栽館

◁　云墙　　　白壁
　　The Cloud Wall.

◁　楠木厅的窗格
　　The patterned window of the
　　Algerbia Hall.

　　楠木庁の窓櫺

△ 五峰仙馆，又称楠木厅。

The Celestial Hall of Five Peaks, also called "the Algerbia Hall".

五峰仙館は楠木庁とも言われる

▷ 揖峰轩内景

The inside of the Worshipping
Stone Pavilion.

揖峰軒の内景

◁　雪后的鸳鸯厅窗户
　　The window of the Mandarin
　　Ducks' Hall after snow.
　　雪後の鴛鴦庁の窓

△　林泉耆硕之馆前后两厅,故又称鸳鸯厅。
　　The Old Hermit Scholars' Hall is divided into halves.
　　Hence the name "the Mandarin Ducks' Hall".

　　林泉耆硕之館は又鴛鴦庁とも言われる

49

▽ 窗景

A window picture.

花窓の風景

◁ 窗景

A window picture.

花窓の風景

△ 漏窗

A latticed window.

漏窓

▷▷ 冠云峰，为苏州园林中最高的太湖石峰。

The Cloud-Capped Peak, the highest Lake Tai limestone in the classical gardens of Suzhou.

冠雲峰——蘇州諸園林にある一番高くて優れている太湖石

▷ 漏窗
  Latticed windows
  漏窗

▷ 留园秋色
  The Lingering Garden
  in autumn.

  留園の秋色

三、网师园

网师园位于苏州古城东南部,占地约 9 亩。为江南园林中的精品。1982 年被列为全国重点文物保护单位。

这里原是南宋侍郎史正志"万卷堂",园名"渔隐"。清乾隆年间,宋氏购得后重新浚池叠石,筑室构堂,沿史氏"渔隐"义,名"网师小筑"。

网师园是一座保持了苏州旧时世家完整的宅、园相联风貌的居住生活区。全园分为东部住宅区、中部山水花园、西部别院。东部厅堂布局严整,结构轩昂,装修雅洁;中部池水清澄,假山雄峻,亭台轩阁环池而筑;西部殿春簃,原为书院,80 年代初中国赴美建造的纽约大都会艺术博物馆内"明轩",即以此处为蓝本设计。

Ⅲ. The Master-of-Nets Garden

Situated in the southeastern part of the old city of Suzhou, the Master-of-Nets Garden, covering about 5,400 sq. m, is the finest specimen of the classical gardens in the south of the Lower Yangtze. In 1982 it was listed as cultural relics of national importance. During the Southern Song Dynasty(the late 12th century), the Deputy Minister Shi Zhengzhi abode right in this place with a garden known as "the Fisherman's Retreat", and a private library called "the Hall of 10,000 Volumes". In the middle years of the reign of Qianlong, Song Zongyuan purchased and remodeled the garden – residence, and borrowed the meaning of the Fistherman's Retreat and named it the Master-of-Nets Garden. It is an example of combining living quarters with a landscape garden, a true to type garden-residence belonging to the nobility in Suzhou. There're three parts: the eastern housing area, the central landscape garden and the western garden court. Constructed in accordance with the strict regulations of feudal-

ism, halls and rooms in the east are magnificentbuildings with extraordinary furnishings and interior decoration. The central landscape garden possesses im-
posing man-made mountains and a crystal clear pond curved round by pavilions
and roofed walkways. The western garden court with the Peony Study is the
model for the Astor Court and Ming Room installed by the Chinese in the early
1980s in the Metropolitan Museum of Art, New York City, U. S. A.

三、網師園

　網師園は蘇州の旧市街区の東南側に位置し、約 1800 坪の敷
地面積を持ち、江南園林の珍宝で、1982 年に全国重要文化財に
指定されている。ここは元々南宋時代の侍郎（官職）史正志の
"万巻堂"で、"漁隠"という園名であった。清代の乾隆年間、宋
宗元がこれを手に入れてから、池を浚渫し、石で築山を築き、庁
堂楼閣を建築し、史正志の"漁隠"という園名のニアンスを取っ
て、"網師園"に改名したのである。

　網師園は蘇州旧時の高官の住宅と庭園とを一つ結びついた
佇いが完璧に保存されて来たものである。その東部は住宅部
分で、中部は山水の庭で、西部は別院である。東部の建築物の
配置は厳密で、構造は堂々たるもので、飾りは古風で優雅なも
のである。中部の池水は澄み切り、築山は雄大で険しく、亭台
楼閣は皆池を囲んで建てられている。西部の"殿春簃"は元の
書斎であった。八十年代の初期、中国がアメリカのニューヨー
クにある"メトロポリタン芸術博物館"で庭園庭築"明軒"を建
てたが、それは園内の"殿春簃"をモデルにして建てられたもの
である。

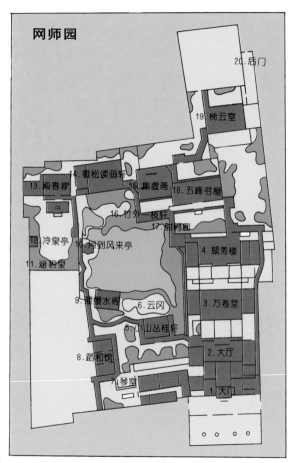

网师园

20. 后门

19. 梯云室

14. 看松读画轩

13. 殿春簃

15. 集虚斋

18. 五峰书屋

16. 竹外一枝轩

17. 射鸭廊

12. 冷泉亭

10. 月到风来亭

4. 撷秀楼

11. 涵碧泉

9. 濯缨水阁

6. 云冈

3. 万卷堂

5. 小山丛桂轩

8. 蹈和馆

2. 大厅

7. 琴室

1. 天门

The Master-of-Nets Garden

1. The main entrance
2. The hall
3. The Hall of 10,000 Volumes
4. The Beauty Within Reach Tower
5. The Small Hill and Osmanthus Fragrans Pavilion
6. The Cloudy Ridge
7. The Music Room
8. The Daohe House
9. The Washing my Ribbon Pavilion over the Water
10. The Moon Comes with Breeze Pavilion
11. Hanbi Spring
12. The Cold Spring Pavilion
13. The Peony Study
14. The Watching Pines and Appreciating Paintings Studio
15. The Meditation Study
16. The Prunus Mume Pavilion
17. The Duck Shooting Corridor
18. The Five Peaks Library
19. The Cloud Stairway Room
20. The back-door

▽ 万卷堂,为园内主客厅。　　　　萬卷堂——園中の主な客間

The Hall of 10,000 Volumes, the main reception hall of the Master-of-Nets Garden.

▽ 撷秀楼内陈设
　　Furnishings of the Beauty
　　Within Reach Tower.
　　撷秀楼内部の調度類

▽ 门楼上部砖雕人物故事
　　Carved historical figures, the upper part
　　of the earthen door ornamenta tion.
　　煉瓦彫刻の人物

▷ 园内的砖雕门楼
　　A door richly carved with earthen
　　ornamentation in the Master-of-Nets
　　Garden.
　　煉瓦彫刻の屋根

▽ 门楼上部侧面的砖雕　　屋根の両側の煉瓦彫刻

The upper section of the carved earthen door ornamentation.

▽ 四面窗户的小山丛桂轩，为观景娱乐之所。

With windows on four sides, the Small Hill and Osmanthus Fragrans Pavilion is a place for viewing and entertainment.

四面庁の小山丛桂軒——景色の観賞と娯楽をする場所

◁ 小石桥

A bridge of stone.

小さい石橋

△ 环绕中部水池的假山、濯缨水阁和月到风来亭。
The central pond is curved round by man-made mountains, the Washing the Ribbon of my Hat Pavilion and the Moon Comes with Breeze Pavilion.
中部の池水を巡って建てられた築山、濯纓水閣と月到風来亭

▷ 攀附在白墙上的木香花，极有特色。
The white-washed wall partly concealed by Rosa Banksiae Ait. cv. Albo Flena.
白壁に絡みつく木香の花

△ 游廊

A roofed walkway.

廊下

◁ 濯缨水阁

The Washing the Ribbon of my
Hat Pavilion by the pond.

濯纓水閣

△ 雪后的网师园

A snowy view of the Master-of-Nets
Garden.

網師園の雪景色

▷ 鱼乐

Happy fishes.

戯れる魚

△ 竹外一枝轩和射鸭廊位于池水东北部。

The Prunus Mume Pavilion and the Duck Shooting
Corridor are to the north east of the pond.

竹外一枝軒と射鴨楼

▽ 冷泉亭

The Cold Spring Pavilion.

冷泉亭

凌霄花

Campsis grandiflora.

凌霄花

《のうぜんかずら》

窗景

A window picture.

花窗の風景

殿春簃窗景

Window pictures of the
Peony Study.

殿春簃の窓景色

△ 园中小景——石笋

The stone bamboo of the mini-garden within the garden.

園中の小景——石筍

▽ 铺地

The pavement.

舗地

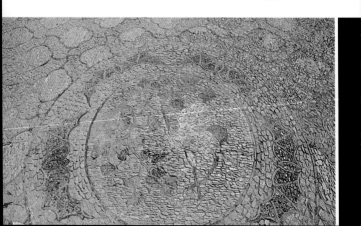

▷ 红枫

The red maple.

紅葉

▷ 梯云室夜色

The Cloud Stairway Room at night.

梯雲室の夜景

四、环秀山庄

环秀山庄,位于苏州城中景德路,面积仅 3 亩,1988 年被列为全国重点文物保护单位。

环秀山庄占地不大,但其内湖石假山为中国之最。据载,此山为清代叠山大师戈裕良的留世之作。假山占地不足半亩,但崖道、山洞、曲涧、石室、磴道、幽谷、峰峦、危径、绝壁曲折回环,宛转多姿,变幻莫测,极尽万壑千岩之妙趣,素有"天然画本"之称。

山下有池水萦绕,山巅有古木参天;山池四周东西有漏窗高墙,南北有四面厅与补秋山房。置身其间,可得真山之天趣、园林之雅韵。

IV. The Mountain Villa with Embracing Beauty

Celebrated for its most wonderful limestone mountain in China , the Mountain Villa with Embracing Beauty, covering about 2, 180 sq. m. , is located on Jing De Road, Suzhou City. According to the historical records, the mountain was designed and piled up by Gu Yuliang, the great master of the Qing Dynasty. Within an area of less than 500sq. m. , the man – made mountain seems to be spontaneous and uncontrived, possessing high peaks, dells, pathways, caverns, stone house, stone steps, ravines, precipices, gullies, bridges and cliffs. There are towering old trees atop, and murmuring streams at the foot of the mountain. Enclosed from the east to the west by the high wall pierced with latticed windows, it has the Make-Up Autumn Galley on the north and the Four – Sided Viewing Hall on the south. Full of unusual and unexpected views, the Mountain Villa with Embracing Beauty Looks like a natural landslape painting. In this false mountain, one is able to enjoy the true delights of the classical garden, and of Mother Nature.

四、環秀山荘

環秀山荘は蘇州の旧市街区の景徳路に位置し、その敷地面積は僅か600坪で、1988年に全国重要文化財に指定されている。

環秀山荘の敷地は広くはないがその内の太湖石の築山は中国一とも言える。記載によるとこの築山は清代の築山大家の戈裕良によって築かれたそうである。築山の敷地面積は100坪足らずが、その崖や洞穴、谷川、山路、深谷、山峰、絶壁、曲がりくねっている険しいトンネルなどが変化に富んでいて、丸で千崖万壑に入ったような感じがする。昔から"天然のスケッチの元"と讃えられてきた。

下には池水が巡り会い、上には天を突くような古木があり、東側と西側には漏窓の作られた高い壁があり、南側と北側にはそれぞれ"四面庁"と"補秋山房"がある。そこに居れば山の趣と園林の真髄は目の保養になり、肌で感じ取ることができるに違いない。

◁◁ 环秀山庄

The Mountain Villa with Embracing

環秀山庄

△ 险路

The awesome mountain
pathway.

険しい小径

▷　石室
The stone house.
石室

◁　曲桥
A zigzag bridge.
曲橋

▷　山洞与小石桥
The ravine and the small
stone bridge.
谷川と小さい石橋

△ 问泉亭

The Putting a Question to the Spring Pavilion.

問泉亭

◁ 从山涧中观问泉亭

A view of the Putting a Question to the Spring Pavilion from the ravine.

谷川のほうから望んだ問泉亭

△ 通过桥、廊将其它建筑和亭、假山巧妙地联结为一体。

The roofed walkway and bridge are unifying man-made mountains, pavilions, and other garden buildings at one breath.

建築物や亭や築山などは橋と廊下で巧みに一つに結びつけられている

五、沧浪亭和狮子林

这是苏州两处历史久远的园林。

沧浪亭，北宋著名诗人苏舜钦建造，面积约 16 亩。园中山上古木参天，山石嶙峋，为典型的"城市山林"。北面与园外小河相傍，自然开朗，为借景之佳例。现园内沧浪石亭，为清代康熙年间建造，亭柱上刻有"清风明月本无价，近水远山皆有情"的楹联，写出了古园的意境。园内多竹，又有清代所建五百名贤祠供人瞻仰。

狮子林，始建于元至正年间，初为寺庙园林。园内大型假山群外表雄浑，内部空灵，洞壑幽深曲折，盘桓有如迷阵，素有"假山王国"之称。清乾隆六次南巡到苏，五次前往，因爱其美景，后分别在避暑山庄、圆明园内仿造。全园结构紧凑，长廊围绕，曲径通幽，楼台隐现。

V. The Canglang Pavilion and the Lion Forest Garden

The Canglang Pavilion and the Lion Forest Garden are two old gardens in Suzhou, each having a very long history. With an area of 10, 656 sq. m., the Canglang Pavilion was laid out by Su Shunqin, the well-known poet of the Northern Song Dynasty. Simple and restrained, the garden has an earthen hill covered with old trees, and with rocks sticking out of it to strengthen the natural effect. The successful combination of the landscape garden inside with a canal outside makes it known far and wide as "typical urban scenery". The Canglang Pavilion made of stone dates back to the reign of Kangxi of the Qing Dynasty. With a view to expressing the designer's artistic conception, the stone pillars of the pavilion are carved with two lines of verse or parallel couplet, saying, "The refreshing breeze and the bright moon are priceless; the nearby water and the distant hills all have tender sentiments." Many varieties of bamboo are unusual features of the garden. In addition, there's a Qing Temple of 500 Sages for people to look at with reverence.

First built in the reign of Zhi Zheng of the Yuan Dynasty, the Lion Forest Garden was originally a Buddhist temple garden. Noted for its labyrinthine mountains with impressive peaks and jogged rocks of grotesque shapes, winding pathways and caverns, partly concealed pavilions, terraces, towers, and a long roofed walkway ringing the entire property, the Lion Forest Garden, densely but harmoniously arranged, has for long had the reputation of being a "Man-Made Mountainous Kingdom". Emperor Qian Long felt affection towards the garden, visited it for five times during his six inspection tours of South China, and copied its marvellous scenes in the Yuan Ming Garden and the Imperial Mountain Resort.

五、滄浪亭と獅子林

滄浪亭と獅子林はどれも蘇州にある歴史の古い庭園である。

滄浪亭は北宋の著名な詩人蘇舜欽が営造したもので、3200坪の敷地面積を持つ。園内の築山は山石が幾重にも重なって奥深く、古木が鬱蒼たるとしていて典型的な"都市山林"である。北側は園外の小川と伴って、自然的に広がっていて借景のよい例になっている。園内の石造りの"滄浪"の亭は清代の康熙年間のもので、両側の柱には"清風と明月は本價無し、近水遠山皆情け有り"という対句があり、古い滄浪亭の意匠をよく表している。園内には竹が多く植えられ、又清代に建てられた"五百名賢祠"もあり、人々の拝見に供している。

獅子林は元代の至正年間に建てられたもので、最初はお寺の庭であった。園内には雄大な築山建築群があり、石峰が幾重に

も重なって、曲がりくねったトンネルが奥深く続いて、全く迷宮に入ったような感じがする。そのため昔から"築山王国"と誉められてきた。清代の乾隆帝が六回南方を巡視した時、その度に蘇州に来たがその内、五回も獅子林に行ったことがある。その美景がいたく気に入って、後ほどそれぞれ避暑山荘と圓明園にイミテーションの築山を築いた。獅子林は構造が緊密で、長廊が巡り、曲がりくねった玉砂利の小道が奥まで通り、楼閣が築山の間に見え隠れしている。

▽ 明道堂的室内陈设
Furnishings of the Ming Dao Hall.
明道堂室内の調度類

▷ 园内的窗景

A window picture of the garden.

園内の花窓の風景

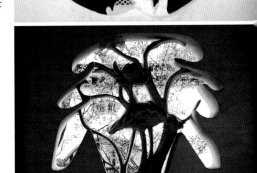

▷ 窗景

A window picture.

花窓の風景

▷ 窗景

A window picture.

花窓の風景

△ 位于园内南部的看山楼　　南側にある看山楼

The Looking at Mountains Tower lies high in the south of the garden.

▽ 清香馆内的根雕家具　　清香館にあるガジマルの根っ子彫刻の調度類

Carved root furniture in the Pure Fragrance Hall.

△ 铺地　　舖地
The pavement.

△ 狮子林内的景色

The scene of the Lion Forest Garden.

獅子林の景色

◁ 燕誉堂内的陈设

Furnishings of the Yan Yu Hall.

燕誉堂内の調度類

◁ 小方厅前的假山
Rockery in front of the Small
Square Hall.
小方庁前の築山

▽ 小方厅
The Smll Square Hall.
小方庁

▷ 立雪堂内的落地罩

The exquisite frame of the Li Xue Hall.

立雪堂にある間仕切り

▽ 立雪堂内陈设

Furnishings of the Li Xue Hall.

立雪堂内の調度類

△ 花篮厅的落地长窗

The long windows of the Flower
Basket Hall.

花藍庁の長窓

◁ 湖心亭

The Mid – Lake Pavilion.

湖心亭

△ 獅子林秋色

The Lion Forest Garden in autumn.

獅子林の秋色

六、艺圃　怡园　耦园

艺圃,位于苏州阊门内吴趋坊文衙弄,为明代大学士文震孟所建。初名"药圃",清代改名"艺圃"。是典型的明代文人山水园,具有幽、静、古、野的特点。

怡园,位于苏州主干道人民路中部,面积约 9 亩,为清同治、光绪年间浙江宁绍台道顾文彬所建。园集苏州诸园特长于一体,又自成一格,故显得格外精美。

耦园,位于苏州城东小新桥巷,一面临街,三面环水。住宅居中,东、西为花园,偶、耦相通,故名。又寓夫妇双归耕织之意。园为清光绪年间两江总督沈秉成退隐而建。其内黄石假山雄浑有势,为园内珍品。

Ⅵ. The Garden of Cultivation, the Garden of Pleasance and the Couple's Garden Retreat

Located in Wen Ya Alley, Wu Qu Fang on the inner side of the Cang Gate of Suzhou, the Garden of Cultivation was built by the Ming Royal Academician Wen Zhenmeng. It was first called "the Herb Garden" and renamed "the Garden of Cultivation" under the Qing Dynasty. Characterized by secluded and serene ambience, archaic and wild appearances, it is an exemplary specimen of landscape gardens of the Ming Dynasty.

The Garden of Pleasance covers 5, 994 sq. m. and lies halfway on arterial Renmin Road. Laid out by Gu Wenbin, the governor of Zhejiang Ningshao during the reign of Tongzhi and the reign of Guangxu, it absorbed all the strong points of other gardens of Suzhou and became a superb garden of its own.

Situated in Xiao Xin Qiao Lane in the eastern part of the city of Suzhou, the Couple's Garden Retreat, fronting the lane, is surrounded by water on three sides. It was built by Shen Bingcheng, the governor of Jiangsu, Anhui and Jiangxi for his retirement years. In choosing this name for the garden, the owner made a play on the original Chinese pictographic character "Ou", meaning "husband and wife ploughing side by side". The magnificant man－made yellowstone moutain gives special prominence to the garden.

六、芸圃、怡園、耦園

芸圃は蘇州閶門内の呉趨坊文衙弄に位置し、明代の大学士文震孟に営造されたものである。最初は"薬圃"という園名であったが、清代に今の"芸圃"と改名された。この庭園は典型的な明代の文人山水園で、優雅で静かで古めかしくて、野趣に富むなどの特色を持っている。

怡園は蘇州のメーン・ストリートの人民路の中部に位置し、敷地面積は約1800坪で、清代の同治、光緒年間に浙江省寧紹台道(官職)顧文彬に営造されたものである。怡園は蘇州の各庭園の特徴を集めたが、又独自の風格を持っているため、その素晴らしさが一入目立つわけである。

耦園は蘇州市内の東側の小新橋巷に位置し、その一面は横道に面し、ほかの三面は皆水に臨んでいる。住宅は真ん中に位置するがその東と西の両側は庭になっている。偶と耦は諧声で、又野良仕事と織り場の夫婦が共に帰宅の意味も潜められているから、耦園と名付けられたのである。耦園は清代の光緒年間(江蘇省と浙江省の)両江総督の沈秉成が引退して建てたものである。園内の黄石によって築かれた築山は雄渾で勢いに富み、園内の珍品と成している。

△ 耦园的洞门

The moon gate of the Couple's Garden Retreat.

耦園の洞門

△ 耦园载酒堂

The Carrying Wine Hall in the Couple's Garden Retreat.

耦園の載酒堂

▷ 耦园内的黄石假山

The man-made yellowstone mountain in the Couple's Garden Retreat.

耦園にある黄石の築山

△ 怡园红枫

The red maple of the Garden of Pleasance.

怡園の紅葉

▽ 秋日的怡园

The Garden of Pleasance in autumn.

秋の怡園

◁ 藕香榭内陈设

Furnishings of the Lotus Fragrance Pavilion.

藕香榭内の調度類

△ 怡园内的复廊

The double verandahs in the Garden of Pleasance.

怡園の復廊

▽ 独具一格的花窗

Uniquely pictured windows.

一風変わった花窓の風景

▽ 独具一格的花窗

Uniquely pictured windows.

一風変わった花窓の風景

▷ 怡园内的画舫

The Fancy Boat in the Garden of Pleasance.

怡園の画舫

△ 艺圃的庭院典雅清秀

The elegant Garden of Cultivation.

芸圃の優雅で秀麗な庭

▷ 艺圃园内太湖石
The limestones in the Garden of
Cultivation.

芸圃にある太湖石

▽ 南斋一景
The scene of the South Study.

南斎の一景

△ 乳鱼亭为园内观鱼佳处　　乳魚亭——魚を観賞する最適の場所
The Fry Pavilion, a nice place for watching fishes.

▽ 艺圃假山和乳鱼亭　　芸圃の築山と乳魚亭
The man-made mountains and the Fry Pavilion in the Garden of Cultiva tion.

七、退思园、燕园、启园、渔庄与高义园

苏州有些园林建在城区之外。

退思园,坐落在苏州南郊同里镇。清光绪年间官僚任氏所建,取"退思补过"意名。园自东而西,横向布局,别具一格。园中水池宽广,春、夏、秋、冬、琴、棋、书、画,各景点贴水而置,有"贴水园"之称。

燕园,在常熟古城内,清乾隆年建。建筑精致,布局紧凑,山石玲珑,尤以"燕谷"黄石假山驰名江南。

启园,位于东山翁巷村北的太湖之滨,背山面湖,自然山水兼收园内。现园内有明代柳毅井、清代古杨梅等胜迹。

建于明末清初的渔庄,在苏州西南郊石湖景区内。园傍石湖而建,近水远山、风帆轻舟交织成一幅江南水乡图。

乾隆南巡敕建的高义园,位于苏州西郊天平山麓。该园依山而筑,简朴古雅。

Ⅶ. The Tuisi Garden, the Swallow Garden, the Xis' Garden, the Yus, Village and the Garden of Righteousness.

Some classical gardens are situated outside the city of Suzhou.

Located at Tongli Township to the south of Suzhou, the Tuisi Garden, which means "retreat and meditate upon mending one's ways", was constructed by Ren Lansheng, a retired military commander in the reign of Guang Xu. Uniquely laid out on an east-west axis, it is a waterscape garden with scenic spots and buildings carefully arranged close to the wild expanse of a lake. There are places in the garden for people to enjoy the cyclical loveliness of spring, summer, autumn and winter, and to satisfy the needs of reading, painting, playing chess and performing on a musical instrument.

Built in the reign of Qian Long of the Qing Dyansty, the Swallow Garden is in the old city of Changshu. With elegant buildings neatly fitted, it is famous for its astonishing yellowstone mountain scenery called "Swallow Valley" in the south of the Lower Yangtze.

Laid out against the East Hill in Weng Xiang Village and by the side of Lake Tai, the Xis' Garden succeeds in borrowing the scenery from the outside. It has Liu Yi Well dating from the Ming Dynasty and Mytica rubras sieb etzucc that has survived but is looked upon as belonging to the Qing Dynasty.

Set up by the end of the Ming Dynasty and the beginning of the Qing Dynasty, the Yus' Village is located in the southwestern suburbs of Suzhou by the Stone Lake scenic area . With nearby water, distant hills, sailing-vessels and sculling boats, it forms a fantastic picture of the water country south of the Lower Yangtze.

Constructed at the foot of Tian Ping Hill to the west of Suzhou by a decree from Emperor Qian Long during his inspection tour of South China, the Garden of Righteousness has the features of being simple, plain, archaic and refined.

七、退思園、燕園、啓園、漁庄と高義園
　蘇州の一部の園林は郊外に営造されている。
　退思園は蘇州の南側の郊外の同里鎮に位置し、清代の光緒年間任という官僚に営造されたものである。園名は"退いて思い、過を補う"から取ったものである。東から西へと横の方向に配置されたこの庭は別に情緒が有る。園内には広い池があり、春、夏、秋、冬、琴、棋、書や画などの景観のどれも皆水際に構築されているから"貼水園"とも言われる。

燕園は清代の乾隆年間に常熟の旧市街区に営造されたものである。建築物は緊密に配置され、精緻を極め、山石が玲瓏たるとしているもので、殊に黄石によって積み重ねられた"燕谷"と言う名の築山は江南に於いても名高いものである。

　啓園は東山翁巷村の北側の太湖の水際に営造されたもので、山を背に太湖に臨み、自然の山水の景色を皆園内に収めている。今園内には、明代の柳毅井戸と清代の楊梅の木などがある。

　明末清初に営造された漁庄は蘇州西南側の郊外の石湖風致区に位置している。水に臨み、山も見え、帆掛け船が目の前を航行していて、恰かも一幅の江南の山水の墨絵のように見える。

　南方を巡視した乾隆帝の命令で構築された高義園は蘇州西側の郊外の天平山麓に位置している。高義園は山に沿って築かれ、簡潔で古めかしくて優雅な建築物である。

△ 江南名园——退思园

The famous Tuisi Garden in the south of the Lower Yangtze.

江南の名園——退思園

◁ 退思园退思草堂

The Thatched Cottage of Tuisi in the Tuisi Garden.

退思園内の退思草堂

◁ 退思园中的"天桥"

The Celestial Bridge in the Tuisi Garden.

退思園内の"天橋"

◁ 退思园眠云亭

The Sleeping Cloud Pavilion in the Tuisi Garden.

退思園の眠雲亭

△ 启园
The Xis' Garden.
啓園

▽ 渔庄福寿堂
The Good Fortune and Long Life Hall in the Yus' Village.
漁庄の福寿堂

▷ 高义园戏楼
The stage in the Garden of Righteousness.
高義園の舞台

△ 高义园秋色

The Garden of Righteousness in autumn.

高義園の秋色

◁ 燕园黄石假山

The man-made yellowstone mountain
in the Swallow Garden.

燕園にある黄石の築山

八、残粒园、五峰园、可园、鹤园、听枫园与北半园

这是几处面积较小，不太为人所知，而又各有特色的园林。

残粒园，始建于清代，在苏州诸园中面积最小，因巧于布置，故十分精美，以"小中见大"著称。

五峰园，始建于明代，园中五座太湖石峰均为石中精品，相传为北宋朱勔养植园遗物。

可园，位于沧浪亭对面，原系宋代沧浪亭一部分，现分开。清道光年间重修，为书院园林。

鹤园，在城中韩家巷，与曲园、听枫园相邻。园小巧紧凑、花木扶疏，峰石绕池，简洁幽雅。

听枫园，位于城中庆元坊，晚清金石书画考据家吴云所建。"宅居不广，却有花木之胜。"在苏州小型园林中，以玲珑精致见长。

北半园，位于白塔东路，清乾隆年建，占地仅一亩半，其厅、舫、榭、廊、亭等建筑均以"半"为特色，十分小巧精美。

Ⅷ. The Vestigial Garden, the Five Peaks' Garden, the Passable Garden, the Crane Garden, the Listening to Maple Garden and the Northern Half Garden

These small gardens are not well known, but each of them has its own characteristics.

First built in the Qing Dynasty, the Vestigial Garden, the smallest of all the classical gardens of Suzhou, is so skilfully spaced and arranged that it seems to be large.

Lain out in the Ming Dynasty, the Five Peaks' Garden is named after five fine Lake Tai limestones believed to be taken from the Botanical Garden beionging to Zhu Mian in the Northern Song Dynasty.

The Passable Garden was originally part of the property of the Canglang Pavilion on the opposite side of the alleyway. Repaired in the reign of Dao Guang of the Qing Dynasty, it was an independent school garden.

The Crane Garden is located in Han Jia Lane, Suzhou City, being near to the Zigzag Garden and the Listening to Maple Garden. With rocks lining its pond's edge, the small, elegant and peaceful Crane Garden is tastefully decorated with flowers and trees.

Lying at Qing Yuan Fang, Suzhou City, the Listening to Maple Garden, noted for its wonderful flowers and trees, was laid out by Wu Yun, a late Qing connoisseur of bronze, stone-carving, painting and calligraphy, Small as it is, the Listening to Maple Garden is brought into a high state of perfection.

With an area of only one and a half mu(999 sq. m.), the Northern Half Garden on Bei Ta Dong Road dates back to the reign of Qian Long. The garden is of great excellence with its pavilions, rooms, halls, land boat, corridor and everything making a feature of "half".

八、残粒園、五峰園、可園、鶴園、聴楓園と北半園
　これらの庭園は敷地面積が割合と狭いので、あまり人々に知られていないが各々の特色を持っている。
　残粒園は清代に営造されたもので、蘇州の各庭園でその敷地面積が一番狭いが見事に配置され、こじんまりとしているため"小の中から大が見える"特色で有名である。
　五峰園はその五つの太湖石はどれも立派なものなである。言い伝えによるとそれは北宋の朱勔の養植園に置かれた遺物だそうである。

可園は滄浪亭の向かい側に位置している。元は宋代の滄浪亭の一部分であったが今は別々になっている。清代の道光年間に重修されたことがあり、書院式の園林である。

　鶴園は蘇州旧市街区の韓家巷に位置し、曲園、聴楓園と隣合っている。鶴園もこじんまりとしていて、花や木がいっぱい植えられ、石峰が池の周りに配置されて、簡潔で優雅な所在である。

　聴楓園は蘇州旧市街区の慶元坊に位置し、清代の末期頃の金石書画鑑定家の呉雲に営造されたものである。"居宅は広くはないが花木の勝が有る"。蘇州の小型園林の中で、聴楓園はその精巧を極め、玲瓏たる作りが優れるものである。

　北半園は蘇州白塔東路に位置し、清代の乾隆年間に営造されたものである。敷地面積は僅か300坪のこじんまりとした北半園の特徴は、ホール、画舫、亭、廊下などの建築物がみな半分に建てられていることにある。

△ 鹤园

The Crane Garden.

鶴園

▷ 听枫园
  The Listening to
  Maple Garden.
  聽楓園

▷ 残粒园
  The Vestigial
  Garden.
  殘粒園

▷ 曲园春在堂
  The Lasting Spring
  Hall in the Zigzag
  Garden.
  曲園の春在堂

▷ 可园
The Passable Garden.
可園

△ 西园
The West Garden.
西園

◁ 北半园
The Northern Half Garden.
北半園

△ 置于织造府内瑞云峰,为太湖石名石之一。

The Auspicious Cloud Peak in the garden of the Suzhou Textile Bureau, one of the famous limestones from Lake Tai.

瑞雲峰——四大名太湖石の一つ

九、虎丘(拥翠山庄、万景山庄)

虎丘,位于苏州古城西北部,是著名的风景区,有"吴中第一名胜"之称。宋代苏东坡曾有"到苏州不游虎丘,乃憾事也"之说。虎丘历史悠久,文化遗迹遍布,至今仍有春秋吴王阖闾的墓葬、五代砖结构的云岩寺塔、元代的断梁殿、憨憨泉、千人石、试剑石、陆羽井、生公讲台等名胜。

拥翠山庄,在虎丘山南坡,为一封闭式的山地园林,其内轩、堂、亭、台均依山势随意赋形,既有真山之气,又有园林之趣。

万景山庄,位于虎丘山东南麓,原是一片树林,八十年代初在此建成一座仿古园林,以展示苏派盆景精品为主。

IX. The Tiger Hill (the Verdurous Mountain Villa and the Mountain Villa with 10, 000 Scenes)

Lying to the northwest of the old city of Suzhou, the Tiger Hill is the most famous sight of the region. With a long history, the Tiger Hill boasts many cultural relics and objects such as the Tomb of the Wu King Helu (the Spring & Autumn period), the Yunyan Temple Pagoda (the Fire Dynasties period), the Broken Beam Temple (the Yuan Dynasty), Hanhan Spring, the Thousand Men Rock, the Sword Testing Stone, Lu Yu Well, Shen Gong Platform, etc. "It would be a pity if you had been to Suzhou but didn't visit the Tiger Hill", the Song poet Su Shi said.

The Verdurous Mountain Villa is an enclosed terraced garden on the southern hillside. Its pavilions, halls and paved area are laid out following the natural contours of the Tiger Hill. It has not only the scenery of the hill but also the charm of the garden.

The Mountain Villa with 10, 000 Scenes was built in imitation of a classical garden in the early 1980s on the southeastern side of the woody hill to display the finest Suzhou style bonsai.

九、虎丘（擁翠山庄、万景山庄）

虎丘は蘇州西北側の郊外に位置し蘇州一の風致区で"呉中一の名勝"とも称されている。宋代の名詩人蘇東坡は"蘇州に至りて虎丘を遊ばずんば憾事なりけり"と歌った。虎丘は歴史が悠久で、文化遺跡があまねくある。今にでもまだ春秋時代呉王闔閭のお墓があり、五代の煉瓦作りの雲岩寺塔、元代の断梁殿及び憨々泉、千人石、試剣石、陸羽井戸や生公講台などの名勝があなたの観光を待っている。

擁翠山庄は虎丘の南側の坂にあり、封じられたような山地園林である。その建築物、ホール、亭や台などは皆丘の地勢によって構築され、山の勢いもあれば園林の趣もある。

万景山庄は虎丘の東南側の麓にある。元々は林であったが八十年代の初期、古典園林のように改築されて、主に蘇州盆景の中の上等なものを展示するのに用いる。

△ 虎丘雪景

The snowy scene of the Tiger Hill.

虎丘の雪景色

▽ 剑池
The Sword Pool.
剑池

△ 拥翠山庄内景色
The scene in the Verdurous Mountain Villa .
擁翠山庄の景色

◁ 拥翠山庄
The Verdurous Mountain Villa.

擁翠山庄

117

▽ 万景山庄万松堂

The 10, 000 Pines' Hall in the Mountain
Villa with 10, 000 Scenes in spring.

万景山庄の万松堂

◁ 万景山庄盆景园

The Bonsai Garden in the Moutain Villa
with 10,000 Scenes.

万景山庄の盆栽館

△ 万景山庄春色

The Mountain Villa with 10, 000
Scenes in spring.

万景山庄の春色

Geographical Position of the Classical
Gardens of Suzhou

1. The Humble Administrator's Garden

2. The Lingering Garden

3. The Master-of-Nets Garden

4. The Mountain villa with Embracing
   Beauty

5. The Canglang Pavilion

6. The Lion Forest Garden

7. The Garden of Pleasance

8. The Couple's Garden Retreat

9. The Garden of Cultivation

10. The Five Peaks' Garden

11. The Passable Garden

12. The Northern Half Garden

13. The Smooth Garden

14. The Zigzag Garden

15. The Vestigial Garden

16. The West Garden

17. The Tiger Hill

18. The Verdurous Mountain Villa

19. The North Temple Pagoda

20. The Auspicious Light Pagoda

21. Panmen Gate

22. Wumen Bridge

23. The Hanshan Temple

24. The Train Station of Suzhou

25. The Long Distance Bus Station

26. The Landing Place

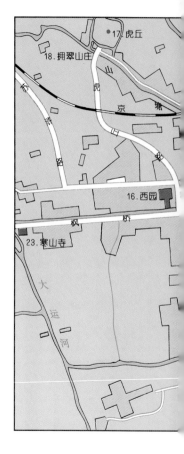

苏州园林分布示意图(城区)

1. 拙政园
2.
3. 网师园
4. 环秀山庄
5. 沧浪亭
6. 狮子林
7. 怡园
8. 耦园
9. 艺圃
10. 五峰园
11. 可园
12. 北半园
13. 畅园
14. 曲园
15. 残粒园
19. 北寺塔
20. 瑞光塔
21. 盘门
22. 吴门桥
24. 苏州站
25. 长途汽车站
26. 轮船客运站

中华名胜导游系列画册

（中、英、日文对照）

☆ 故宫	☆ 黄山
☆ 颐和园	☆ 桂林山水
避暑山庄	☆ 长江三峡
布达拉宫	泰山
曲阜	庐山
☆ 苏州园林	峨眉山
五台山	☆ 九寨沟
☆ 秦兵马俑	☆ 武陵源
☆ 长城	☆ 杭州西湖

（中国旅游出版社将陆续出版）　　☆：已出版

苏州园林（中、英、日文）

（中华名胜导游系列画册）

中国旅游出版社出版发行

深圳彩视电分有限公司制版

利丰雅高印刷（深圳）有限公司印刷

889×1194　1/64

2002年6月第二版第三次印刷

ISBN 7－5032－1312－4
————————————————
K·229

印数：3000　　　　02900